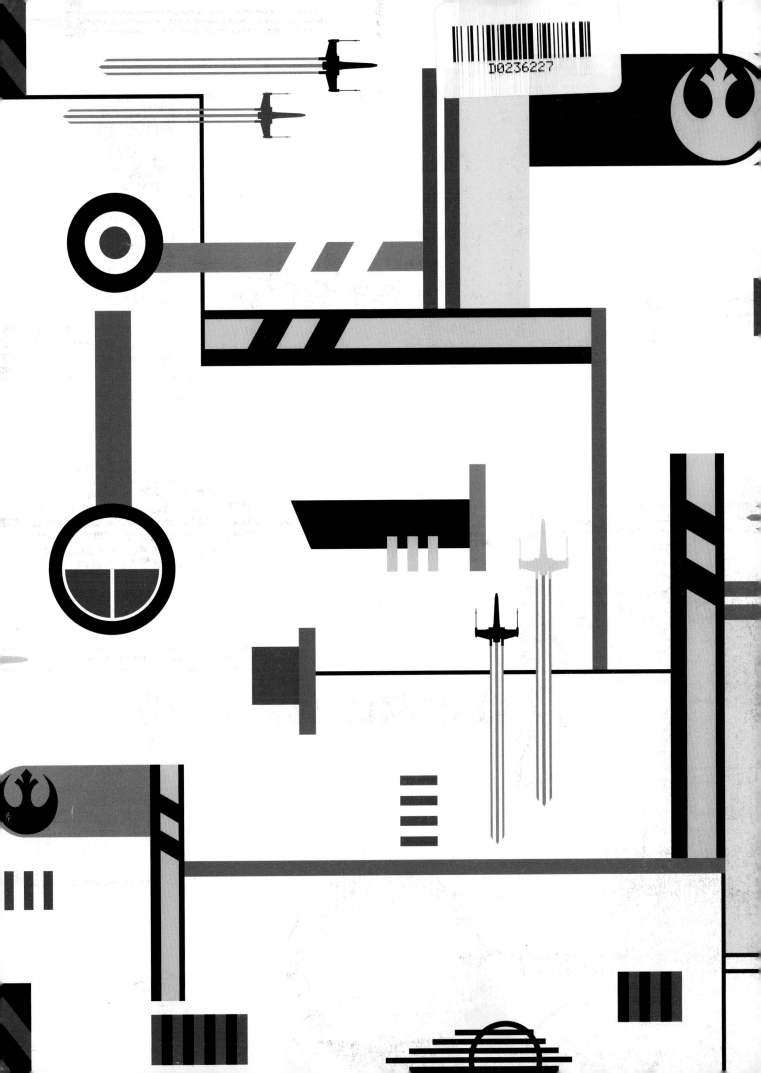

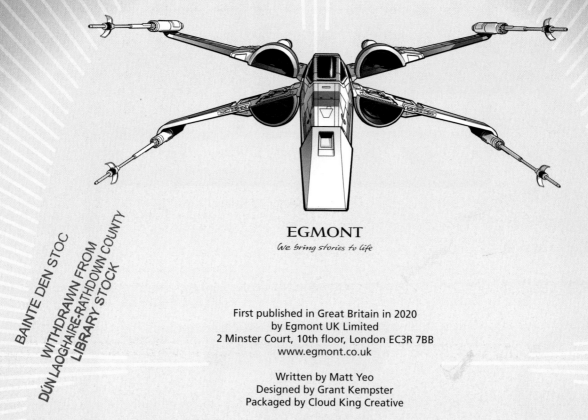

EGMONT
We bring stories to life

First published in Great Britain in 2020
by Egmont UK Limited
2 Minster Court, 10th floor, London EC3R 7BB
www.egmont.co.uk

Written by Matt Yeo
Designed by Grant Kempster
Packaged by Cloud King Creative

© & TM 2020 Lucasfilm LTD.

To find more great *Star Wars* books, visit www.egmont.co.uk/starwars

Egmont takes its responsibility to the planet and its inhabitants very seriously. We aim to use papers from well-managed forests run by responsible suppliers.

ISBN 978 1 4052 9730 1
70902/001
Printed in Italy

THIS ANNUAL BELONGS TO...

NAME:

o llie

SPECIES:

human

HOMEWORLD:

Ereth

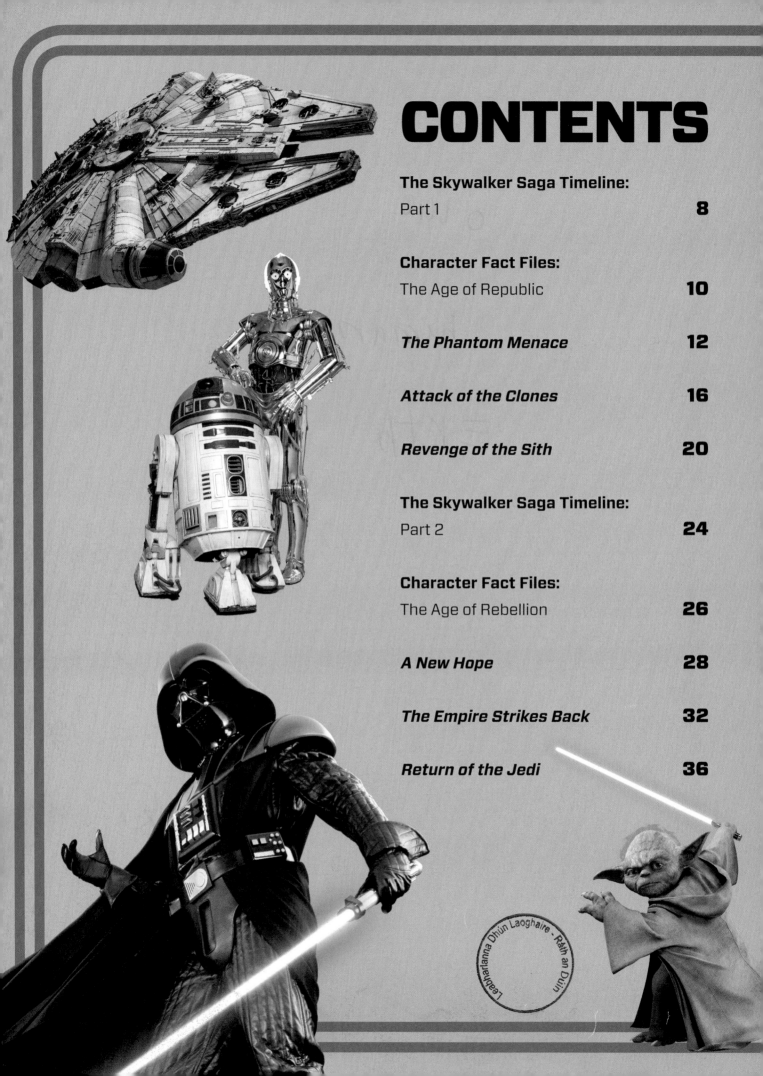

CONTENTS

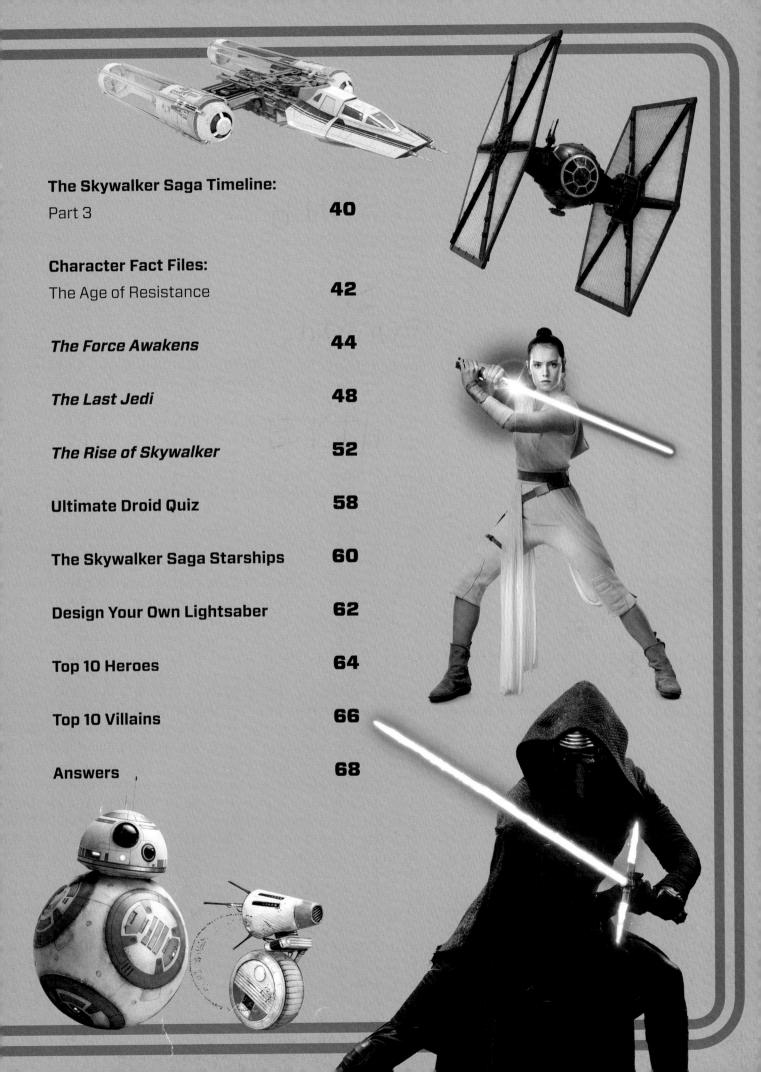

THE SKYWALKER SAGA
TIMELINE – PART 1

The history of the *Star Wars* galaxy has seen empires rise and fall, villains vanquished and heroes triumphant. This timeline shows the most important events that have shaped the epic Skywalker saga from start to finish....

Anakin Skywalker born

Anakin wins Boonta Eve Classic podrace

Darth Maul defeated; Qui-Gon Jinn dies

Attack of the Clones
Obi-Wan discovers clone army on Kamino

The Phantom Menace
Trade Federation blockade of Naboo

Palpatine elected Supreme Chancellor

Jedi attack droid factory on Geonosis

The Jedi discover the Sith have returned

Palpatine creates Grand Army of the Republic; Clone Wars begin

Anakin turns to the dark side and becomes Darth Vader

The Republic becomes the Galactic Empire

Anakin loses hand in battle with Count Dooku

Obi-Wan battles and defeats General Grievous

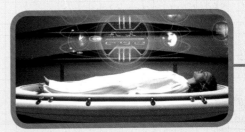

Revenge of the Sith

Battle of Coruscant; Count Dooku defeated

Palpatine revealed to be Darth Sidious

Padmé dies giving birth to twins, Luke and Leia

Padmé Amidala marries Anakin in secret

CHARACTER FACT FILES:
THE AGE OF THE REPUBLIC

Find out all about your favourite characters from a long time ago in a galaxy far, far away....

ANAKIN SKYWALKER

Species: Human
Homeworld: Tatooine

Prophesised to be the Chosen One who would bring balance to the Force, Anakin Skywalker ultimately turned to the dark side and became the sinister Darth Vader.

OBI-WAN KENOBI

Species: Human
Homeworld: Stewjon

Jedi Master and Padawan to Qui-Gon Jinn, Obi-Wan Kenobi fought in the Clone Wars beside Anakin. Years later he was struck down by his friend in a final duel on the Death Star.

QUI-GON JINN

Species: Human
Homeworld: Coruscant

Wise Jedi Master Qui-Gon Jinn was trained by Count Dooku. He was defeated by the Sith Lord Darth Maul during an epic lightsaber battle on Naboo.

PADMÉ AMIDALA

Species: Human
Homeworld: Naboo

Queen and senator of Naboo, Padmé fell in love with and secretly married Anakin Skywalker. She was also the mother of the twins, Luke and Leia.

JAR JAR BINKS

Species: Gungan
Homeworld: Naboo

Once an outcast from his own people, clumsy Gungan Jar Jar became a hero to his people during the invasion of Naboo. He later represented his planet in the Galactic Senate.

DARTH MAUL

Species: Dathomirian Zabrak
Homeworld: Dathomir

A highly-skilled Sith warrior who wielded a unique double-bladed lightsaber, Darth Maul met his match against Obi-Wan Kenobi on Naboo when he was sliced in half.

EMPEROR PALPATINE/ DARTH SIDIOUS

Species: Human
Homeworld: Naboo

Leading a secret double life, Supreme Chancellor Palpatine was in fact the evil Darth Sidious. He restored the Sith and transformed the Republic into the first Galactic Empire.

COUNT DOOKU/ DARTH TYRANUS

Species: Human
Homeworld: Serenno

Originally a trusted Jedi Master trained by Yoda, Dooku was seduced by the dark side and became Darth Tyranus. He led the Separatist army against the Republic.

R2-D2 AND C-3PO

Species: Droid
Homeworld: Tatooine and Naboo

Protocol droid C-3PO and astromech R2-D2 became lifelong companions after they first met on Tatooine. They have shared many adventures together over the years.

YODA

Species: Unknown
Homeworld: Unknown

Nearly 900 years old, Jedi Master Yoda was small in size, but extremely wise with an incredibly strong connection to the Force. He fought in the Clone Wars and led the Jedi Council.

MACE WINDU

Species: Human
Homeworld: Haruun Kal

Champion of the Jedi Order, Master Windu carried a lightsaber with an amethyst blade. He became extremely suspicious of Palpatine, who he believed was corrupt.

JANGO FETT

Species: Human
Homeworld: Unknown

Hired by Count Dooku, bounty hunter Jango Fett was the genetic template for the Republic's clone army. He was also father to his own clone son, Boba Fett.

DARK SIDE DRAWING

Complete this picture of Darth Maul by copying what's in the boxes on the left on to the blank spaces on the right. When you've finished, you can colour in the image!

USE THE FORCE!

Which character from *The Phantom Menace* is in this distorted image? Clear your mind and let the Force flow through you....

Qui gon Jinn

THE PHANTOM WORD SEARCH

Can you find all of the hidden names in this tricky word search? See how fast you can locate them all!

O	M	A	N	L	T	A	K	A	N	A	H	T	A	L
P	P	S	A	G	U	N	G	A	N	T	K	A	T	I
O	J	A	R	R	A	A	A	S	I	Y	O	T	N	G
D	A	G	D	P	T	K	M	S	P	O	O	O	A	H
R	R	A	A	M	R	I	A	H	D	D	B	O	S	T
A	J	E	R	D	E	N	D	N	T	A	A	I	E	S
C	A	R	O	O	A	A	A	I	O	R	N	N	B	A
E	R	A	S	T	T	I	M	A	H	A	A	E	U	B
R	B	O	L	T	A	U	D	I	U	K	M	D	L	E
D	I	N	R	A	R	G	K	A	D	O	S	A	B	R
A	N	O	M	W	P	N	I	A	E	A	R	K	A	O
S	K	Y	W	A	L	K	E	R	G	N	L	L	N	Z
D	S	O	C	O	R	U	S	C	A	N	T	A	P	K
N	B	J	E	D	I	K	N	I	G	H	T	J	A	K
N	G	K	Y	L	F	J	R	C	B	Y	E	U	S	A

- ANAKIN
- SKYWALKER
- PADMÉ AMIDALA
- NABOO
- JAR JAR BINKS
- SEBULBA
- WATTO
- PODRACER
- TATOOINE
- CORUSCANT
- JEDI KNIGHT
- SITH
- DARTH MAUL
- YODA
- LIGHTSABER
- GUNGAN

JUMBLED-UP JAR JAR

Look closely at this mixed up image of Jar Jar Binks and try to put the pieces in the correct order. Write the sequence below.

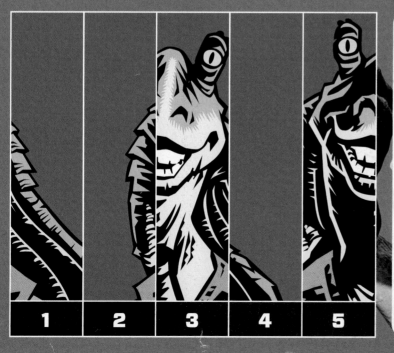

| 1 | 2 | 3 | 4 | 5 |

Answers on p69

BATTLE DROID ODD ONE OUT

These Trade Federation B1 battle droids are powered up and ready for action! They may all look the same, but one of them is a little different. Can you work out which droid is the odd one out?

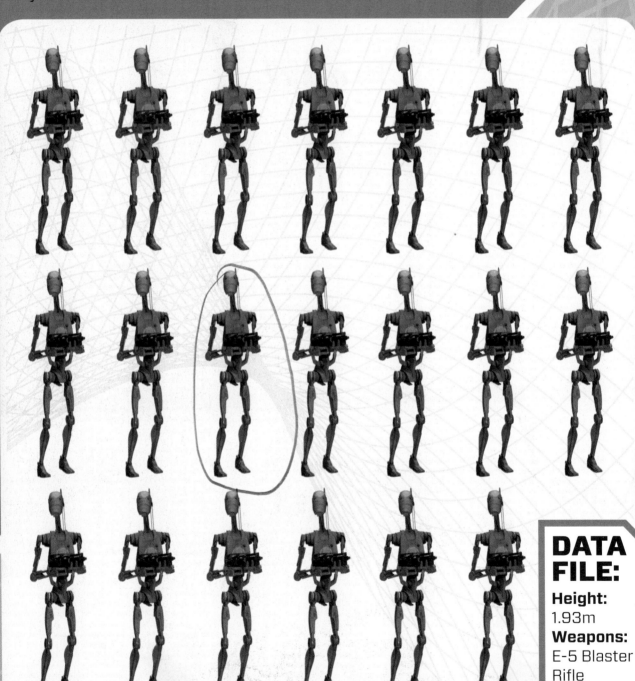

DATA FILE:

Height:
1.93m

Weapons:
E-5 Blaster Rifle

Creator:
Geonosians

Answer on p69

14

STAR WARS™

THE PHANTOM MENACE

ATTACK OF THE CLONES

MAKE A CLONE TROOPER MASK

Help defeat the Trade Federation's droids by joining the Grand Clone Army of the Republic!

INSTRUCTIONS

1. Cut out or copy this page when you've completed the activities on page 18.

2. Stick it on to a piece of stiff card

3. Cut around the helmet and cut out the eye and side holes

4. Thread string through the side holes and then tie a knot

5. Wear your helmet mask into battle!

Ask an adult to help you when using scissors!

JEDI MIND TRICK

The dark side of the Force is clouding your thoughts! Concentrate and see if you can work out which powerful Jedi this is....

DROID ID

Trade Federation droids are attacking! Use all of your training to unscramble the letters below and write the correct names of the clunkers in the boxes.

A

KDAEDIOR

B

RESPU LETBAT ORDID

C

TABLET IDODR

LIGHTSABER BLADES

Each lightsaber contains a special Kyber crystal that gives the ancient weapons their unique colour. Write the names of the correct lightsaber blade colours below!

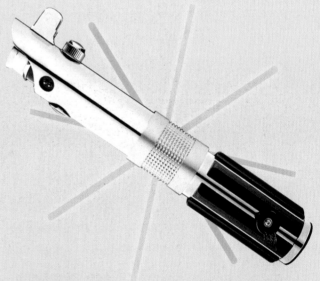

 Count Dooku's lightsaber blade is:

 Yoda's lightsaber blade is:

green

 Anakin Skywalker's lightsaber blade is:

red

 Mace Windu's lightsaber blade is:

 Obi-Wan Kenobi's lightsaber blade is:

BOUNTY HUNTER PURSUIT!

Can you help Jango Fett track Obi-Wan's Jedi starfighter to Geonosis? Follow the routes carefully as only one will lead to your elusive Jedi target!

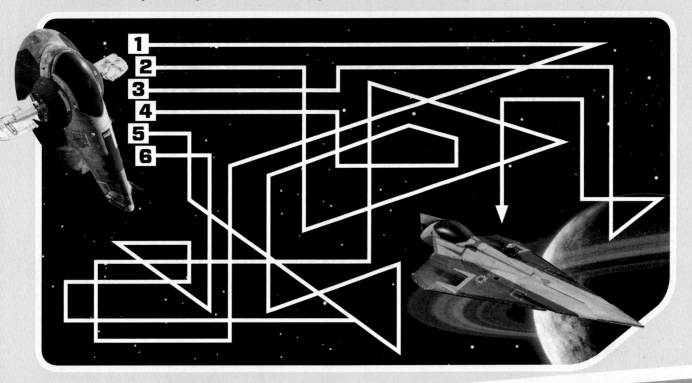

1
2
3
4
5
6

BUILD A DROID

Can you work out which numbered droid parts below you'll need to build an Astromech that looks just like R2-D2?

3 6 5 7

1

2

3

4

5

6

7

8

9

Answers on p69

CLONE TROOPER HELMETS

Clone troopers of the Grand Army have all sorts of different armour and paint designs. Can you match the names to the correct helmets below?

A  B  C  D  E

1 212TH ATTACK BATTALION

2 CLONE TROOPER

3 327TH STAR CORPS

4 SHOCK TROOPER

5 501ST LEGION

HIDDEN LIGHTSABER

Can you find Yoda's lightsaber hidden somewhere in this picture? Look closely and then circle the lightsaber when you find it.

BATTLE READY!

Look carefully at the sequences below and then work out which Separatist character comes next. Write the letters in the blank boxes.

A
B
C

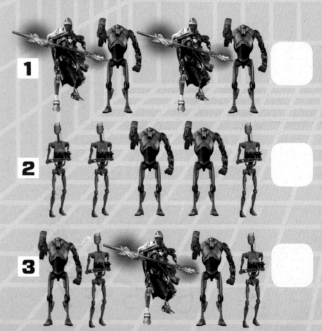

FROM JEDI TO SITH

Anakin Skywalker has become Darth Vader! Guide the Dark Lord of the Sith to Mustafar for his final duel with Obi-Wan Kenobi.

START

FINISH

SCANNER MALFUNCTION!

A Separatist attack on Coruscant has knocked out the Republic's scanners! Take a look at these two images of Republic ships in battle and see how many differences you can spot.

Answers on p69

REVENGE OF THE CROSSWORD

Fit all of the words into the grid below. Ignore any spaces in the words – just include the letters. How many can you fill in?

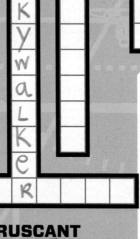

CORUSCANT
ANAKIN SKYWALKER
MUSTAFAR
JEDI MASTER
SITH LORD
OBI-WAN KENOBI
DARTH SIDIOUS
GENERAL GRIEVOUS

DARTH VADER
REPUBLIC
SEPARATISTS
MACE WINDU
COUNT DOOKU
KASHYYYK
MAGNAGUARD

Answers on p69

STAR WARS

REVENGE OF THE SITH

THE SKYWALKER SAGA
TIMELINE – PART 2

Obi-Wan was struck down in lightsaber duel with Darth Vader

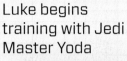

Luke begins training with Jedi Master Yoda

A New Hope

Princess Leia hides Death Star plans in R2-D2

Alderaan destroyed by Death Star

The Empire Strikes Back

Rebel Alliance sets up new base on ice world of Hoth

Obi-Wan Kenobi starts Luke Skywalker's Jedi training

Battle of Yavin; Luke destroys the Death Star

Battle of Hoth; Rebels flee base

Luke, Han Solo and Chewbacca free Leia from the Empire

Han Solo
frozen in
Carbonite

Return of the Jedi
Han Solo rescued; Jabba the
Hutt and Boba Fett defeated

Luke tells
Leia they
are twins

Anakin saved
by Luke;
Together
they defeat
the Emperor

Emperor Palpatine attempts
to lure Luke to the dark side

Battle of
Endor;
Rebels
destroy
the
second
Death
Star

Luke discovers his father is Darth
Vader, loses hand in battle

Rebels join forces with
Ewoks on Endor

Lando Calrissian betrays
his friends to the Empire

CHARACTER FACT FILES:
THE AGE OF REBELLION

With the galaxy under the tyranny of the Empire, a brave Rebellion emerged to challenge the darkness....

LUKE SKYWALKER

Species: Human
Homeworld: Tatooine

A Tatooine farm boy and Rebel hero who became one of the greatest Jedi ever. Luke was also an ace X-wing pilot and the son of Anakin Skywalker.

HAN SOLO

Species: Human
Homeworld: Corellia

Captain of the legendary *Millennium Falcon*, scoundrel and smuggler, Han Solo joined the fight against the Empire and fell in love with Princess Leia.

PRINCESS LEIA

Species: Human
Homeworld: Alderaan

Luke's twin sister, Leia was raised as royalty by her adopted family on Alderaan. She was a tough leader and fighter who battled against the tyranny of the Empire.

CHEWBACCA

Species: Wookiee
Homeworld: Kashyyyk

Co-pilot of the *Millennium Falcon* and Han Solo's Wookie friend. Chewie is also an excellent mechanic and extremely strong, but really hates losing games of holochess.

LANDO CALRISSIAN

Species: Human
Homeworld: Socorro

Baron Administrator of Cloud City, Lando joined the Rebellion and became a general. He flew the *Millennium Falcon* and helped destroy the second Death Star.

DARTH VADER

Species: Human
Homeworld: Tatooine

Anakin Skywalker betrayed the Jedi Order and turned to the dark side to serve his master Palpatine and the Empire. He was ultimately saved and brought back to the light by his son, Luke.

JABBA THE HUTT

Species: Hutt
Homeworld: Nal Hutta

A powerful gangster who ruled his criminal empire from a palace on Tatooine. Jabba met his untimely end when he unsuccessfully attempted to feed Luke Skywalker to a sarlacc.

BOBA FETT

Species: Human
Homeworld: Kamino

The clone son of Jango Fett, Boba was known throughout the galaxy as a fierce and menacing bounty hunter. He successfully captured Han Solo and delivered him to Jabba the Hutt.

WEDGE ANTILLES

Species: Human
Homeworld: Corellia

Brave X-wing pilot Wedge flew with the Rebel Alliance from its earliest days, battled the Empire on Hoth and helped destroy both Death Stars.

WICKET W. WARRICK

Species: Ewok
Homeworld: Endor

Brave Ewok warrior Wicket helped the Rebel Alliance take down the second Death Star's shield generator on Endor, allowing them to blow up the battle station.

TIE FIGHTER ATTACK!

The Empire has launched TIE fighters against the Rebel forces! However, one of the ships is slightly different from the rest of the squadron. Can you spot which one it is?

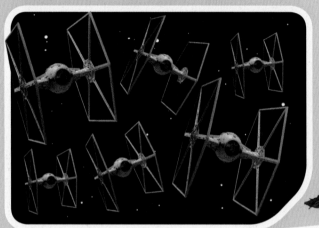

DROID SALE

This pesky Jawa is trying to sell you second-hand droids, but can you work out which ones? Take a look at the close-up images and write your answers below.

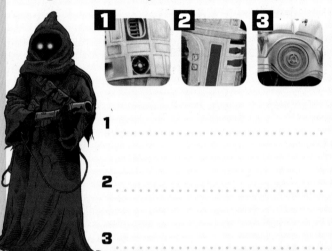

1 ....

2 ....

3 ....

STARSHIP SCRAMBLE

It's time to pilot your ships and take the battle to the enemy! Draw a line from each character to their correct ship.

DARK SIDE DOT TO DOT

Connect the dots to reveal the identity of one of the Galactic Empire's most fearsome agents! Write the name of the character once you've completed the picture.

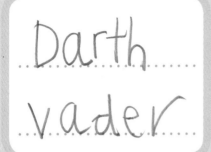

Darth vader

PRINCESS LEIA: TRUE OR FALSE?

Rebel leader, diplomat and brave fighter. Princess Leia is all of these and much more. But how much do you know about her? Take a look at the questions below and tick yes or no for each answer.

1 Princess Leia's home planet is Tatooine.

2 Princess Leia's ship is the *Tantive IV*.

3 Princess Leia wears a white gown.

4 Princess Leia's Death Star detention cell number is 2187.

5 Princess Leia's last name is Organa.

6 Princess Leia's father is called Han.

7 Princess Leia tells the Empire the Rebels are on Dantooine.

8 Princess Leia hides the Death Star plans in C-3PO.

9 Princess Leia uses a lightsaber.

10 Princess Leia dives into the trash compactor last on the Death Star.

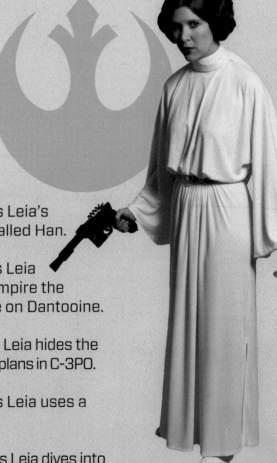

Answers on p69

DEATH STAR ESCAPE!

Help guide C-3PO and R2-D2 safely through this challenging Death Star maze and escape in the *Millennium Falcon*. How fast can you flee from the Empire?

START

FINISH

Answer on p69

STAR WARS™

A NEW HOPE

STAR WARS™

THE EMPIRE STRIKES BACK

REBEL CODES

The Empire is searching the galaxy for the Rebel Alliance's hidden base, so all X-wing pilots must send messages in code! Use the key below to work out what the secret messages are.

A	B	C	D	E	F	G	H	I	J	K	L	M

N	O	P	Q	R	S	T	U	V	W	X	Y	Z

(coded message 1)

(coded message 2)

(coded message 3)

(coded message 4)

(coded message 5)

Answers on p69

33

AT-AT ATTACK!

The Empire has discovered the Rebel's hidden base on the ice planet of Hoth! Quickly – take a look at these two AT-AT pictures and see how many differences you can find between them.

DATA FILE:

All Terrain Armoured Transports, or AT-AT walkers, are four-legged combat vehicles used by Imperial ground forces on rough terrain.

JEDI TRAINING SUDOKU

It's time to start your Jedi training on Dagobah with Master Yoda! Draw pictures in the grids so that each column and each row contains only one of each symbol.

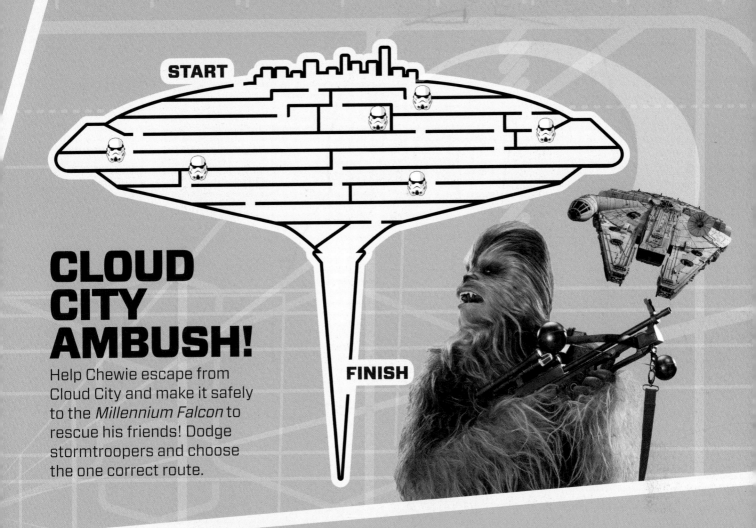

START

FINISH

CLOUD CITY AMBUSH!

Help Chewie escape from Cloud City and make it safely to the *Millennium Falcon* to rescue his friends! Dodge stormtroopers and choose the one correct route.

SYMBOL SEQUENCES

Take a look at these Rebel and Imperial patterns, then write or draw the missing character in each row. How quickly can you correctly complete each sequence?

 A

 B

C

D

Answers on p69

35

FEEDING TIME!

Jabba the Hutt's favourite pet is hungry and needs a tasty treat! Find your way through this tricky maze and see how long it takes you to reach the rancor and feed it a snack.

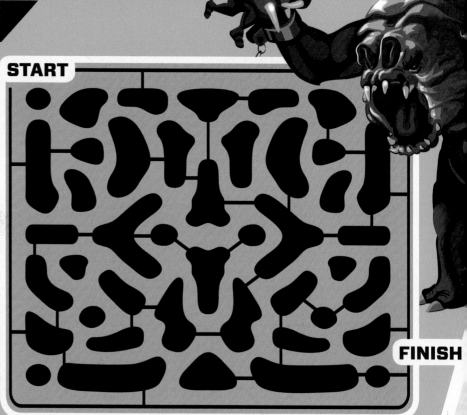

START

FINISH

WHAT'S THAT VEHICLE?

Take a good look at these scavenged vehicle parts and see if you can figure out which craft they're from. Fill in the blank letters to complete the names of each vehicle.

 Tl_ in_erce_tor

 Y-__ng

 S_eed_r bi_e

MESSED UP MESSAGE!

R2-D2 is carrying an important message from Luke Skywalker for Jabba the Hutt, but his hologram projector is damaged! Unscramble the letters to reveal what Luke is saying.

ERLASEE NAH LOOS

LUKE SKYWALKER VS DARTH VADER

It's Jedi father versus son in an epic lightsaber battle to the finish!
But can you put these scenes from *Return of the Jedi* in the right order?

1

2

3

4

ROGUE SQUADRON MEMORY GAME

The best Rebel Alliance pilots need to have a good memory to make it in to Rogue Squadron! Study this picture for 60 seconds, cover it and answer as many questions as possible.

1 How many X-wings are in the picture?

2 What colour are the Imperial laser blasts?

3 Which moon is below the battle?

4 Which side of the picture is the second Death Star on?

5 What colour are the X-wing laser blasts?

Answers on p69

FIND THE EWOKS!

It's time for the Ewoks to strike back! Take the battle to the Empire on the Forest Moon of Endor and see if you can find the six Ewoks hidden in this picture.

Answers on p69

STAR WARS

RETURN OF THE JEDI

The Force Awakens
Stormtrooper FN-2187 leaves the First Order, encounters Poe Dameron

Battle of Takodana; Rey captured by Kylo Ren

Han Solo struck down by his son; Rey fights and injures Kylo Ren

The Last Jedi
The Resistance flees base on D'Qar

Starkiller Base destroys Hosnian System

Finn meets Rey and BB-8, travel to Takodana with Han Solo and Chewbacca

Starkiller Base destroyed; Rey travels to Ahch-To to find Luke Skywalker

Luke initially refuses to train Rey as a Jedi, but eventually agrees to show her the ways of the Force

Finn, Rose and BB-8 search for a hacker on Canto Bight

C-3PO has memory wiped on Kijimi; heroes travel to remains of second Death Star

Captain Phasma defeated by Finn; then he rejoins his friends for the Battle of Crait

The Rise of Skywalker
Emperor Palpatine revealed to be alive on Exegol

Resistance forces battle Sith fleet over Exegol; Rey defeats Palpatine

Luke Skywalker becomes one with the Force after the battle on Crait

Rey battles Kylo Ren on the remains of the Death Star on Kef Bir; Ben Solo rejects the dark side

Kylo Ren strikes down Snoke, becomes Supreme Leader

Rey, Finn, Poe, Chewie and droids race to find a clue to the location of a Sith Wayfinder on Pasaana

Ben gives his life to save Rey; First Order defeated and peace returns to the galaxy

CHARACTER FACT FILES:
THE AGE OF RESISTANCE

Years after the defeat of the Empire, the First Order rose to power. Only a new generation of heroes can save the galaxy once and for all....

REY

Species: Human
Homeworld: Jakku

A scavenger living on Jakku, Rey soon discovered she had a much larger destiny. She trained with Jedi Master Luke Skywalker to learn the ways of the Force.

FINN

Species: Human
Homeworld: Unknown

As a stormtrooper, FN-2187 served the First Order, but soon broke away to join the Resistance. Poe gave him the name 'Finn' before their escape to Jakku.

POE DAMERON

Species: Human
Homeworld: Yavin 4

A skilled pilot and fighter, Poe was also a Resistance commander. He helped lead the attack on Starkiller Base and was one of Leia Organa's best operatives.

BB-8

Species: Droid
Homeworld: Hosnian Prime

A friendly and loyal astromech, BB-8 has been on many missions with Poe Dameron. He is equipped with all sorts of tools and gadgets which come in very handy.

MAZ KANATA

Species: Unknown
Homeworld: Takodana

Impossibly old, Maz Kanata lived in an equally ancient castle on Takodana where she mixed with smugglers and pirates. Maz gifted Luke's lightsaber to Rey.

ROSE TICO

Species: Human
Homeworld: Hays Minor

A skilled maintenance tech and engineer, Rose and her sister Paige joined the Resistance soon after the First Order attacked and decimated their homeworld.

ZORII BLISS

Species: Human
Homeworld: Kijimi

Leader of the Spice Runners of Kijimi, Zorii shared a past with Poe Dameron. However, she couldn't stay neutral for long once the First Order had destroyed the planet.

JANNAH

Species: Human
Homeworld: Unknown

Formerly a stormtrooper known as TZ-1719, Jannah left the First Order with the rest of her squad to eventually settle on the planet Kef Bir, the ocean moon of Endor.

SUPREME LEADER SNOKE

Species: Unknown
Homeworld: Exegol

Once believed to be the ultimate power behind the First Order, Snoke was revealed to have been a mere puppet created by a rejuvenated Emperor Palpatine.

GENERAL HUX

Species: Human
Homeworld: Arkanis

A ruthless officer, Hux believed the First Order's technological might would be more than a match for the Resistance. He had a strong rivalry with Kylo Ren.

KYLO REN

Species: Human
Homeworld: Chandrila

Formerly Ben Solo, he turned against his family and Jedi Master Luke Skywalker and became a servant of darkness. Ren carried a unique and deadly red-bladed crossguard lightsaber.

CAPTAIN PHASMA

Species: Human
Homeworld: Parnassos

Wearing special chromium armour, Captain Phasma was commander of the First Order's stormtrooper legions. She was defeated in battle against Finn.

STARSHIP IDENTITY

Check that your scanners are working and see if you can unscramble and match the correct names of these six Resistance and First Order starships.

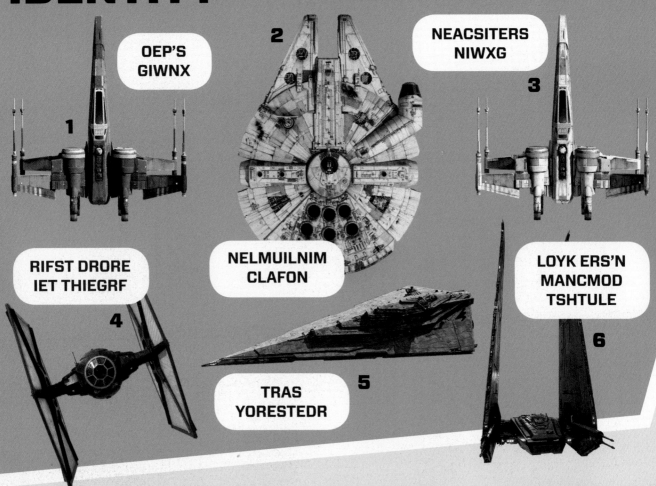

OEP'S GIWNX

2

NEACSITERS NIWXG

3

1

RIFST DRORE IET THIEGRF

4

NELMUILNIM CLAFON

LOYK ERS'N MANCMOD TSHTULE

6

5

TRAS YORESTEDR

SCRAMBLED TROOPER

This First Order stormtrooper helmet image is all scrambled up! Look closely at it and then write the correct letter sequence in the box below.

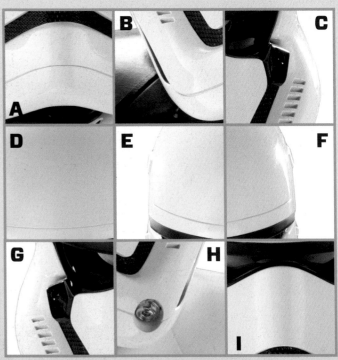

A | B | C
D | E | F
G | H | I

	D	

SYMBOL MATCH

Draw a line to match the Resistance and First Order symbols with the correct characters.

FIRST ORDER ESCAPE

Help the *Millennium Falcon* escape from the clutches of the First Order! Follow the correct line to make it safely back to the Resistance base on D'Qar.

1

2

3

Answers on p69

COLOUR YOUR OWN BB-8

BB-8 needs a brand new paint job. Use all of your favourite colours to fill him in!

DATA FILE:
ELITE PRAETORIAN GUARDS

Supreme Leader Snoke is protected at all times by his Elite Praetorian Guards. These mysterious and highly-trained warriors wear red armour and wield a variety of lethal weapons.

Bilari Electro-Chain Whip

Twin Vibro-Arbir Blades

Vibro-Voulge

Electro-Bisento

FORCE CHALLENGE

Use your Jedi training to find all of the hidden items in this main picture. When you've found them, write the grid coordinates in the blank boxes.

3A	Porg # 1
	Porg # 2
	BB-8's head
	Stormtrooper helmet
	BB-9E

NAME THE CHARACTERS

Can you correctly identify these five characters?
Try timing yourself to see how quickly you can guess them all!

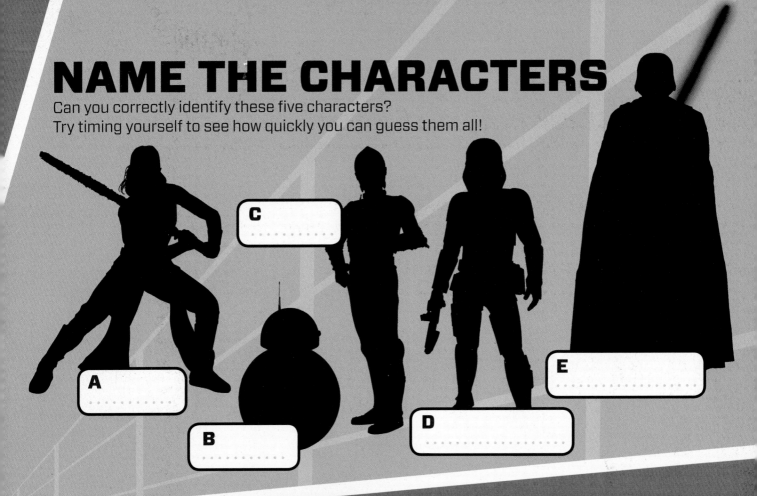

C

A

B

D

E

CANTO BIGHT CASH IN

Finn and Rose have hit the jackpot on Canto Bight! Help them work out how much their winnings total by adding up the chip amounts.

Green = 1 credit

Red = 5 credits

Blue = 10 credits

Yellow = 50 credits

Purple = 100 credits

KYLO REN'S LIGHTSABER

Kylo Ren's journey to the dark side is nearly complete and all he needs is his lightsaber. Can you work out which is the correct one?

1
2
3
4
5

Answers on p69

49

SPOT THE DIFFERENCE

Can you spot six differences between these two porg pictures? You'll need to look closely to find them all!

DATA FILE:

Porgs are small, flat-muzzled avians that live on the rocks and cliffs of Ahch-To. They are very inquisitive little creatures.

Answers on p69

STAR WARS
THE LAST JEDI
™

STAR WARS
THE RISE OF SKYWALKER

While the Resistance slowly rebuilds itself, the galaxy is shocked to learn that Emperor Palpatine is still alive and hiding in the Unknown Regions. Presumed dead decades earlier, the Sith Lord has been scheming in secret and offers Supreme Leader Kylo Ren the might of a massive Star Destroyer fleet if he will serve his new master.

The Resistance realises this will be its ultimate battle, but the only way to reach Palpatine on Exegol is by locating a device called a Sith Wayfinder. Together, Rey, Finn, Poe, Chewie and the droids travel to find one on Pasaana. With the help of Lando Calrissian they find the device. Barely escaping, the heroes next head to Kijimi, where they meet an old friend of Poe's, Zorii Bliss. She helps them have C-3PO reprogrammed so he's able to reveal the location of another Wayfinder on the moon of Kef Bir. This is where part of the second Death Star landed and Rey finds the device before battling and beating Ren with the help of Leia, who dies using the last of her energy.

Rey uses the Force to save Ren's life, then heads to face the Emperor. Seeing a vision of his father, Ren turns from the dark side and becomes Ben Solo again. Rey and Ben eventually face the might of the reborn Palpatine together, while Resistance ships attempt to stop the Star Destroyers of the Final Order. Rey ultimately defeats the Sith Lord and Ben uses his life force to save her.

With the Final Order and Palpatine defeated at last, Rey has one more task to complete. She heads to Tatooine to bury Luke and Leia's lightsabers, before taking on the surname, Skywalker. The heroes have saved the day and light has finally returned to the galaxy!

DATA FILE:
THE KNIGHTS OF REN

These mysterious armoured warriors answer only to Supreme Leader Kylo Ren himself. Each is armed with lethal close and long range combat weapons. They all wear different armour and helmets and are Force-sensitive.

VICRUL

CARDO

KURUK

AP'LEK

USHAR

TRUDGEN

DAMAGED D-O

Poor D-O! It looks like his main uni-tread disc has been damaged in battle. Can you work out which of these replacement discs below is the correct one?

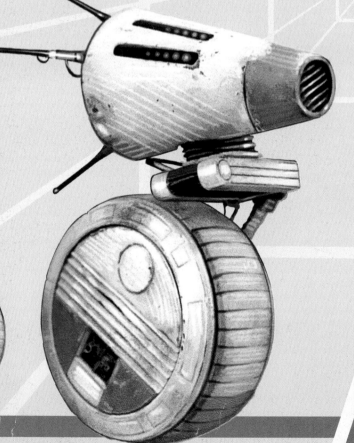

A

B

C

D

THE FINAL BATTLE

Emperor Palpatine is eager to unleash the might of the First Order and Sith fleet on an unsuspecting galaxy! Can you match the correct names to the pictures?

TIE DAGGER

SITH TROOPER

SITH JET TROOPER

TIE WHISPER

TAKE OUT THE TOWER!

Finn and Jannah are on a last ditch mission to save the galaxy! Help them place the explosives in the correct locations to destroy the Star Destroyer's communications tower.

1	2	3	4
5	6	7	8

Answers on p69

SUPREME MASK MAZE

Kylo Ren's helmet has been reforged through Sith alchemy. See how fast you can make it through this tricky maze!

START

FINISH

Answer on p69

STAR WARS
THE RISE OF SKYWALKER

™

ULTIMATE DROID QUIZ!

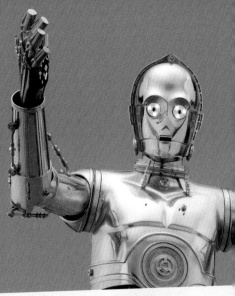

I am C-3PO, human-cyborg relations. In my many adventures across the galaxy, I have encountered all kinds of mechanical marvels. The information on these droids is stored in my databanks and prepared for you here as a galactic challenge. How many questions can you answer correctly?

1 Is C-3PO fluent in over six or ten million forms of communication?

2 What are destroyer droids also known as?

3 Is the Trade Federation droid factory located on Kamino or Geonosis?

4 Did a protocol droid discover the hidden Rebel base on Hoth?

5 Is R2-D2 a protocol or astromech droid?

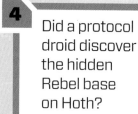

6 Do pit droids repair starships or pod racers?

7 Is C-3PO's left arm gold or red in *The Force Awakens*?

8 Does a 2-1B medical droid heal Luke on Hoth or Endor?

9 Do X-wing fighters have one or two droid sockets?

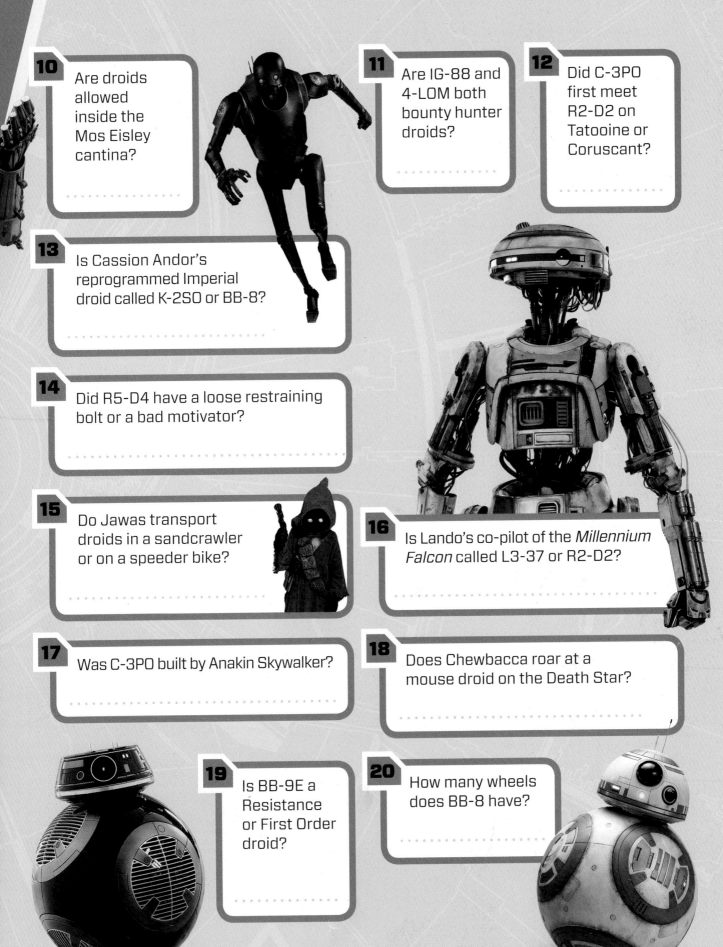

10 Are droids allowed inside the Mos Eisley cantina?

. . . .

11 Are IG-88 and 4-LOM both bounty hunter droids?

12 Did C-3PO first meet R2-D2 on Tatooine or Coruscant?

. . . .

13 Is Cassion Andor's reprogrammed Imperial droid called K-2SO or BB-8?

. . . .

14 Did R5-D4 have a loose restraining bolt or a bad motivator?

. . . .

15 Do Jawas transport droids in a sandcrawler or on a speeder bike?

. . . .

16 Is Lando's co-pilot of the *Millennium Falcon* called L3-37 or R2-D2?

. . . .

17 Was C-3PO built by Anakin Skywalker?

. . . .

18 Does Chewbacca roar at a mouse droid on the Death Star?

. . . .

19 Is BB-9E a Resistance or First Order droid?

. . . .

20 How many wheels does BB-8 have?

. . . .

Answers on p69

THE SKYWALKER SAGA STARSHIPS

From snub-nosed starfighters to hulking capital ships, space battles in the galaxy have been decided by starships of all shapes and sizes.

Affiliation:
Rebel Alliance,
Resistance
Length: 34.37m
Height: 7.9m
Crew: 2-4

MILLENNIUM FALCON

A Corellian YT-1300 light freighter, this legendary smuggler ship served the Rebel Alliance and the Resistance. Once owned by both Lando Calrissian and Han Solo, the *Millennium Falcon* made the Kessel Run in less than 12 parsecs.

X-WING

The Incom X-wing is known throughout the galaxy as a fast and responsive starfighter. The Rebel Alliance used T-65B fighters to take down both Death Stars, while Resistance pilots fly updated Incom-FreiTek T-70 versions.

Affiliation: Rebel Alliance, Resistance
Length: 12.48m-13.4m
Height: 2.4m-2.7m
Crew: 1 pilot, 1 astromech

TIE FIGHTER

The roar of a TIE's engines are unmistakable. These nimble ships are often flown in waves and work together to take down larger targets. Numerous variations include the TIE bomber, interceptor, silencer, whisper, dagger and special forces.

Affiliation: Galactic Empire, First Order, Final Order
Length: 6.3m-17.43m
Height: 3.76m-7.7mm
Crew: 1-2

STAR DESTROYER

These wedge-shaped capital ships were built to instil fear into the galaxy. Packed with weapons, ships and troops, Star Destroyer variants include Super Star Destroyers and planet killing Sith Star Destroyers.

Affiliation: Galactic Empire, First Order, Final Order
Length: 1600m-19000m
Height: 145.7m-682mm
Crew: 48,785-280, 734

Y-WING

A workhorse starfighter that's been used in battles since the Clone Wars. Able to take part in dogfights and bombing runs, the Y-wing is slow but sturdy. Pilots often strip off the outer hull plates to customise them.

Affiliation: Republic, Rebel Alliance, Resistance
Length: 18.17m-23.4m
Height: 2.44m-2.85m
Crew: 1 pilot, 1 Astromech

DESIGN YOUR OWN LIGHTSABER

Traditionally the ancient weapon of a Jedi, lightsabers have also been used by others, such as the Sith. Powered by a unique Kyber crystal, the blade can slice through metal and enemies alike. By using the Force, it's even possible for skilled users to deflect blaster bolts back at their foes with a lightsaber.

ANAKIN SKYWALKER'S LIGHTSABER

The second lightsaber constructed by Anakin, this weapon was passed on to his son, Luke. Believed lost for decades, the lightsaber was eventually given to Rey by Maz Kanata.

KYLO REN'S LIGHTSABER

This crossguard lightsaber has a red ragged blade due to its cracked Kyber crystal. Two side quillions vent excess power, giving the blade its unique appearance.

YODA'S LIGHTSABER

Although he preferred to find peaceful solutions to conflict, Yoda was also one of the greatest lightsaber wielders in the galaxy. His speed and strength in the Force made Yoda a powerful Jedi Master.

DARTH VADER'S LIGHTSABER

When Anakin Skywalker became a Lord of the Sith, he constructed a new lightsaber with a red blade. It would be used to fell Obi-Wan Kenobi and cut off Luke's hand.

Complete your training by designing your own lightsaber! The handle can be any shape and style you like. Will it be a Jedi or Sith lightsaber? What colour will your lightsaber blade be?

TOP 10 HEROES

Where there is darkness there is light and where there are villains there are heroes. These are the top 10 heroes in the whole of the Skywalker saga. Their legends will live on forever!

OBI-WAN KENOBI

Legendary Jedi Master and Padawan to Qui-Gon Jinn, Obi-Wan Kenobi was also a general in the Republic army. He trained Anakin Skywalker and his son, Luke.

ANAKIN SKYWALKER

Born a slave on Tatooine, Anakin was one of the most powerful Jedi ever. A skilled pilot and cunning warrior, he was prophesied to bring balance to the Force.

YODA

Although small in size, Jedi Master Yoda was extremely wise and powerful. He trained Jedi for over 800 years, before going into exile on the swamp planet of Dagobah.

LUKE SKYWALKER

Raised on Tatooine like his father, Luke yearned for excitement and adventure. Joining the Rebellion, he eventually became a Jedi Master and trained Rey.

HAN SOLO

Smuggler and scoundrel, Han Solo was also captain of the *Millennium Falcon* and father to Ben Solo, who would later become Kylo Ren.

PRINCESS LEIA

Daughter of Padmé Amidala and Anakin Skywalker, and twin sister to Luke, Leia Organa was one of the greatest leaders of both the Rebel Alliance and Resistance.

CHEWBACCA

Co-pilot of the *Millennium Falcon*, this 200-year-old Wookiee is extremely loyal to his friends. Captured by the Empire, Chewie was freed from slavery by Han Solo.

FINN

Trained from birth by the First Order to serve as a stormtrooper, FN-2187 quit to become Finn, when he met Rey on Jakku. He soon became a valuable Resistance fighter.

POE DAMERON

Ace pilot Poe Dameron was a spice smuggler before he joined the Resistance. He once flew a black and orange signature X-wing with his droid pal, BB-8.

REY SKYWALKER

Abandoned on Jakku, Rey couldn't remember her parents. A gifted mechanic and pilot, she soon found out she was also powerful in the Force and would one day change the fate of the galaxy.

TOP 10 VILLAINS

When the galaxy is in turmoil, dark forces emerge from the shadows. The top 10 villains in the Skywalker saga are cunning, ruthless and evil. Beware their power!

COUNT DOOKU

Once a Jedi Knight, Dooku turned to the dark side and became Darth Tyranus. He was ultimately defeated in an epic lightsaber battle with Anakin Skywalker.

SUPREME LEADER SNOKE

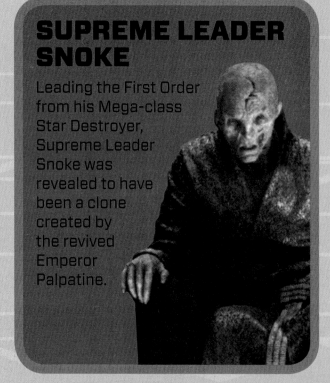

Leading the First Order from his Mega-class Star Destroyer, Supreme Leader Snoke was revealed to have been a clone created by the revived Emperor Palpatine.

GENERAL HUX

Power-hungry and devious, General Hux was ordered by Snoke to work alongside Kylo Ren. When he betrayed the First Order, he was blasted by General Pryde.

GENERAL GRIEVOUS

This vicious cyborg led the Separatist droid armies into battle against the Republic. His four arms allowed him to wield multiple lightsabers at the same time.

JABBA THE HUTT

Known and feared throughout the galaxy, Jabba the Hutt was a powerful gangster. He placed a large bounty on Han Solo and made him a wanted man.

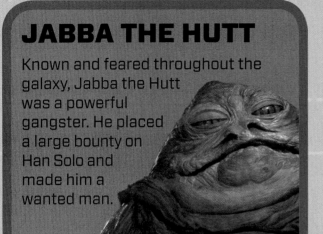

BOBA FETT

Wearing Mandalorian armour, bounty hunter Boba Fett pursued his targets in his infamous ship, Slave I. He met his ultimate fate when he fell into a Sarlacc pit on Tatooine.

KYLO REN

Ben Solo rebelled against his Jedi training and turned to the dark side. He served Supreme Leader Snoke before striking him down.

DARTH MAUL

This fierce Sith warrior was trained by Darth Sidious to defeat the Jedi. He managed to cut down Qui-Gon Jinn, but was beaten in battle by Obi-Wan Kenobi.

DARTH VADER

Beneath the black armour that kept him alive, Vader was once Anakin Skywalker. As the Emperor's right-hand man, he helped Palpatine hunt down the Jedi.

EMPEROR PALPATINE

The ultimate evil in the galaxy. Once thought dead, Palpatine retuned from the grave and attempted to rule once more. He was finally defeated by Rey and Ben Solo.

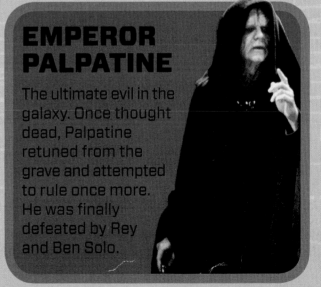

ANSWERS

P12
USE THE FORCE!
Qui-Gon Jinn

P13
THE PHANTOM WORD SEARCH

JUMBLED-UP JAR JAR
2, 5, 3, 1, 4

P14
BATTLE DROID ODD ONE OUT

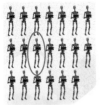

P18
JEDI MIND TRICK
Yoda

DROID ID
A: Droideka
B: Super battle droid
C: Battle droid

LIGHTSABER BLADES
Count Dooku's blade is red
Yoda's blade is green
Anakin's blade is blue
Mace Windu's blade is purple
Obi-Wan's blade is blue

P19
BOUNTY HUNTER PURSUIT!

BUILD A DROID
3, 5, 6, 7

P20-21
CLONE TROOPER HELMETS
A: 5
B: 3
C: 1
D: 2
E: 4

HIDDEN LIGHTSABER

BATTLE READY!
1: A, **2:** C, **3:** A

FROM JEDI TO SITH

SCANNER MALFUNCTION!

P22
REVENGE OF THE CROSSWORD

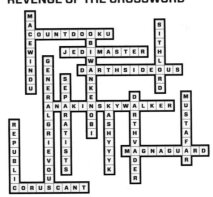

P28
TIE FIGHTER ATTACK!

DROID SALE
1: R2-D2
2: R5-D4
3: C-3PO

STARSHIP SCRAMBLE
A: 3, **B:** 1, **C:** 4, **D:** 2

P29
DARK SIDE DOT TO DOT
Darth Vader

PRINCESS LEIA: TRUE OR FALSE
1 ✗, 2 ✔, 3 ✔, 4 ✔, 5 ✔
6 ✗, 7 ✔, 8 ✗, 9 ✔, 10 ✗

P30
DEATH STAR ESCAPE!

P33
REBEL CODES
Beware the Empire
Dodge the asteroid field
Avoid all probe droids
Jump to hyperspace
Rendezvous on Hoth

P34
AT-AT ATTACK!

JEDI TRAINING SUDOKU

P35
CLOUD CITY AMBUSH!

SYMBOL SEQUENCES

P36
FEEDING TIME!

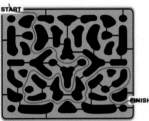

WHAT'S THAT VEHICLE?
TIE interceptor
Y-wing
Speeder bike

MESSED UP MESSAGE!
Release Han Solo

P37
LUKE SKYWALKER VS DARTH VADER
2, 4, 3, 1

ROGUE SQUADRON MEMORY GAME
1: 8, **2:** Green, **3:** Endor,
4: Left, **5:** Red

P38
FIND THE EWOKS!

P44
STARSHIP IDENTITY
1: Poe's X-wing
2: *Millennium Falcon*
3: Resistance X-wing
4: First Order TIE fighter
5: Star Destroyer
6: Kylo Ren's Command Shuttle

SCRAMBLED TROOPER

E	D	F
G	I	C
B	A	H

P45
SYMBOL MATCH

FIRST ORDER ESCAPE

P48
FORCE CHALLENGE
Porg #2 - 7D
BB-8's head - 2C
Stormtrooper helmet - 2A
BB-9E - 2B

P49
NAME THE CHARACTERS
A: Rey
B: BB-8
C: C-3PO
D: Stormtrooper
E: Kylo Ren

CANTO BIGHT CASH IN
421 credits

KYLO REN'S LIGHTSABER
2

P50
SPOT THE DIFFERENCE

P54
DAMAGED D-O
Disc C

P55
THE FINAL BATTLE
1: Sith Jet Trooper
2: TIE Whisper
3: TIE Dagger
4: Sith Trooper

TAKE OUT THE TOWER!
1E
2C
3A
4D
5H
6B
7G
8F

P56
SUPREME MASK MAZE

P58
ULTIMATE DROID QUIZ!
1: Over six million
2: Droidekas
3: Geonosis
4: No
5: Astromech
6: Podracers
7: Red
8: Hoth
9: One
10: No
11: Yes
12: Tatooine
13: K-2SO
14: A bad motivator
15: Sandcrawler
16: L3-37
17: Yes
18: Yes
19: First Order
20: None